Teaching Investigative Skills

Book 1
Ages 7–8

Chris Tooley

Folens Publishers

The author, Chris Tooley, is an Advanced Skills Teacher (AST) working in Cambridgeshire. He has practical experience of working with teachers across a wide range of schools.

Acknowledgements

I would like to offer my thanks to my wife, Joanna, who has been a significant influence in shaping the materials and unstinting in support and encouragement. Also to Shân Oswald, Senior Science Advisor for Cambridgeshire, and all the primary colleagues who played an important part.

United Kingdom: Folens Publishers, Apex Business Centre, Boscombe Road, Dunstable, LU5 4RL.
Email: folens@folens.com

Ireland: Folens Publishers, Greenhills Road, Tallaght, Dublin 24.
Email: info@folens.ie

Poland: JUKA, ul. Renesansowa 38, Warsaw 01-905.

Editor: Rebecca Harman
Layout artist: Patricia Hollingsworth
Cover design: Duncan McTeer
Cover image: Robert Harding Picture Library
Illustrations: Debbie Clarke

First published 2003 by Folens Limited.
Reprinted 2003.

British Library Cataloguing in Publication Data. A catalogue record for this publication is available from the British Library.

ISBN 1 84303 014-4

Contents

Introduction

The materials in this book form the first part of the foundation skills for scientific enquiry at Key Stage 2.

Skills sessions

Lesson plans, OHTs and Pupil Sheets for the following topics:
- Investigating Factors
- What Will Happen?
- Fair Tests
- Tables.

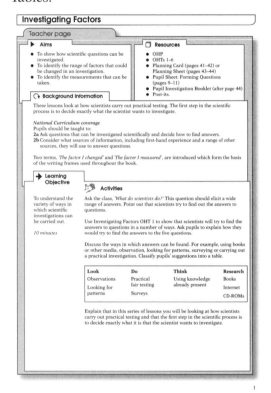

Investigating Factors should be taught first as it introduces the key terms: *'The factor I changed'* and *'The factor I measured'*, which are employed in all later sessions. However, the following sessions may be taught in any order.

Pupil Sheets

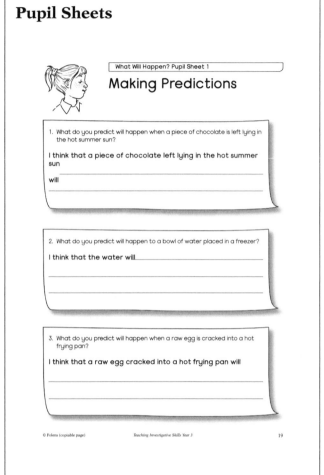

Most skills sessions are accompanied by Pupil Sheets. These worksheets are designed to be photocopied and distributed to individual pupils for the completion of exercises. Writing frames have been used throughout these worksheets to ensure that pupils are able to concentrate on gaining new investigative skills whilst minimising literacy demands.

Practical application sessions

Each skills session is followed by lesson plans, linked to QCA units, detailing the reinforcement of the skills in an overtly scientific and practical context.

At the end of each lesson plan there is a list of other investigative activities that can be used to further embed the skills. These examples have been drawn from the Year 3 QCA units.

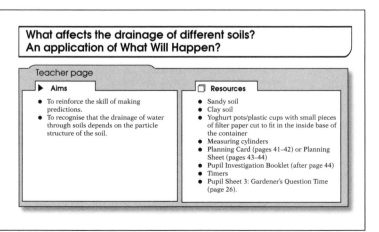

Planning Cards and Planning Sheets

Two discrete resources have been provided to aid the all-important planning process of investigations. Either is suitable for use in the teaching of this skill and all subsequent investigative lessons. However, individual teachers may prefer one or the other format.

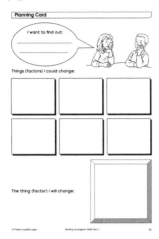

The Planning Card, which can be found on pages 41–42, can be used in conjunction with Post-its to provide pupils with a 'hands on' planning framework for the identification of factors to be investigated. This is best accomplished by photocopying the two pages back to back and then laminating the sheet. This ensures that the cards can be used time after time for any planning activities.

The Planning Sheet, which can be found on pages 43–44, provides a writing frame that pupils can use in two ways. The Planning Sheet can be photocopied and laminated to provide a quick, reusable reference for pupils when writing up an investigation, or the sheet can be photocopied and given to pupils to use as writing frames, which can then be fixed into their science books.

Pupil Investigation Booklet

The Pupil Investigation Booklet for **Year 3** can be found after page 44. To construct the booklet, simply photocopy the four individual sheets back to back and then fold and staple the resulting two sheets.

The booklets can be used in two ways:
- In conjunction with the skills sessions to provide immediate reference to the key learning points and writing frames introduced in the session.
- When carrying out any subsequent practical investigations. The booklets provide a single location where pupils can gain help and reminders when encountering any of the taught skills. Pupils should be encouraged to use this resource rather than immediately asking the teacher as, in this way, pupils can be encouraged to develop a personal working understanding of skills, so becoming increasingly independent in their work.

A copy of the booklet can be given to each pupil so that annotations can be added, or class sets can be made and re-used from year to year.

Background

Origins and development

The materials in this book were developed in response to numerous requests from primary colleagues and advisory teachers for a coherent scheme to teach the skills of scientific enquiry (Sc1).

The following skills are focused on:

- Forming questions

- Predictions

- Planning fair tests

- Tables

- Graphs

- Conclusions

- Evaluations.

These specific skills were chosen for a number of reasons:

- To lay a sound foundation of skills for primary pupils to interact with the scientific knowledge and understanding required at Key Stage 2.

- To reflect the emphasis on Sc1 in the end of Key Stage National Curriculum assessments.

- To enable pupils to approach investigative work with confidence at Key Stage 2 and beyond.

The initial materials, aimed at Year 6 classes, were trialled in a group of over 35 schools. Responses from teachers were positive and further modifications were made to include Year 5. This scheme was then adopted by Cambridgeshire LEA and recommended to all primary schools.

The success of this scheme led to calls for the development of complementary materials for Years 3 and 4. These were duly completed and tested in classroom trials. The whole programme was then revised to form a complete Key Stage 2 scheme.

Classroom trials of the complete Key Stage 2 schemes led to further positive feedback including an OFSTED report that noted, 'this systematic programme is proving an effective foundation for teaching good lessons very sharply focused on scientific skills.'

The nature of the materials

Early discussions with primary school teachers, backed up by a review of published materials, suggested that normal practice for pupils to learn the skills of scientific enquiry was by the following:

- Meeting the skills for the first time within the context of a practical investigation.

- Being asked to deal with several new skills at the same time.

It was found that a more profitable way to introduce these key skills was for pupils to be taught the skills individually and in a context free from the competing 'noise' of practical work. In this way, the skills themselves would take centre stage as the sole learning objective.

Accordingly, each new skill is introduced in a theoretical session, and outlined in a detailed lesson plan using overhead transparencies to communicate new ideas to pupils. Although non-practical, the design of the session and accompanying worksheets has focused upon ensuring that all pupils are actively involved in the learning process.

The application of the skills in practical contexts is vital if pupils are to gain a full understanding of the scientific process. To this end, follow up activities have been developed (referenced to QCA units) to accompany each skills session.

The final components of the materials are the Pupil Investigation Booklets that accompany each year at Key Stage 2. These booklets can be photocopied and used as a first resort, encouraging pupils to develop increasing independence in investigative work.

This structure is most simply described using the diagram below:

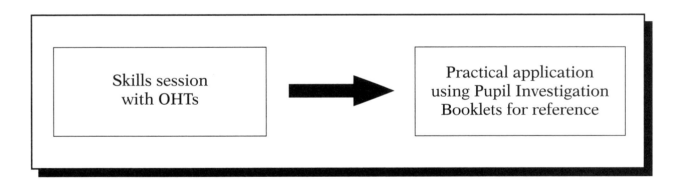

Progression of materials over the key stage

The skills taught in each successive year reinforce and build upon those developed earlier. Years 3 and 4 concentrate on foundation skills, dealing with discontinuous factors (discrete variables), whereas Years 5 and 6 concentrate on the relationships between continuous factors (continuous variables). The culmination of this work comes in Year 6 when pupils are challenged to complete a number of whole investigations. This development can be most clearly appreciated in the table on page viii.

Skill Area	Year 3	Year 4	Year 5	Year 6
Forming Questions	Identifying key factors and introducing the terms, *'The factor I changed'* and *'The factor I measured'*.	Using factors to suggest what will happen in an investigation.	Forming questions for investigation and making predictions.	Using factors to plan fair tests and describing patterns in results.
Predictions	Suggesting the outcomes of a range of circumstances involving discrete factors (variables). Explaining ideas, often using everyday knowledge and understanding.	Making predictions with increasing use of simple scientific facts to explain ideas.	Suggesting the outcomes of a range of circumstances involving continuous factors (variables). Explaining ideas, often using scientific facts.	Making predictions over a range of contexts using scientific facts to justify ideas.
Planning Fair Tests	Identifying the factors to be controlled to make simple, fair tests involving a small number of factors.	With help, planning fair procedures and considering whether tests are fair or not.	Developing clear, step-by-step instructions to fairly investigate questions set by the teacher.	Planning and carrying out fair investigations with increasing independence.
Tables	With help, producing simple tables, mostly involving one series of data.	Increasingly producing simple tables independently (using Pupil Investigation Booklets).	With help, producing tables involving more than one series of data.	Independently producing tables involving more than one series of data (using Pupil Investigation Booklets).
Graphs	With help, producing simple bar graphs.	Producing simple bar graphs with increasing independence (using Pupil Investigation Booklets).	Independently producing simple bar graphs or, with help, line graphs.	With help, producing line graphs.
Conclusions	Saying what was found out in an investigation.	Saying what was found out in an investigation and, increasingly, using simple scientific facts to explain the findings.	Saying what was found out in an investigation and using simple scientific facts to explain the findings.	Identifying and describing patterns found between continuous factors (variables) and using scientific facts to explain these findings.
Evaluations		Looking back at investigative work and suggesting one point that could be improved.	Looking back at investigative work and suggesting two or more points the could be improved.	Considering a whole investigation and suggesting two or more points that could be improved and how it would be done.

Investigating Factors

Teacher page

▶ Aims

- To show how scientific questions can be investigated.
- To identify the range of factors that could be changed in an investigation.
- To identify the measurements that can be taken.

🗎 Resources

- OHP
- OHTs 1–6
- Planning Card (pages 41–42) or Planning Sheet (pages 43–44)
- Pupil Sheet: Forming Questions (pages 9–11)
- Pupil Investigation Booklet (after page 44)
- Post-its.

↺ Background Information

These lessons look at how scientists carry out practical testing. The first step in the scientific process is to decide exactly what the scientist wants to investigate.

National Curriculum coverage
Pupils should be taught to:
2a Ask questions that can be investigated scientifically and decide how to find answers.
2b Consider what sources of information, including first-hand experience and a range of other sources, they will use to answer questions.

Two terms, *'The factor I changed'* and *'The factor I measured'*, are introduced which form the basis of the writing frames used throughout the book.

➡ Learning Objective

To understand the variety of ways in which scientific investigations can be carried out.

10 minutes

✋ Activities

Ask the class, *'What do scientists do?'* This question should elicit a wide range of answers. Point out that scientists try to find out the answers to questions.

Use Investigating Factors OHT 1 to show that scientists will try to find the answers to questions in a number of ways. Ask pupils to explain how they would try to find the answers to the five questions.

Discuss the ways in which answers can be found. For example, using books or other media, observation, looking for patterns, surveying or carrying out a practical investigation. Classify pupils' suggestions into a table.

Look	Do	Think	Research
Observations	Practical fair testing	Using knowledge already present	Books
Looking for patterns	Surveys		Internet
			CD-ROMs

Explain that in this series of lessons you will be looking at how scientists carry out practical testing and that the first step in the scientific process is to decide exactly what it is that the scientist wants to investigate.

Investigating Factors

→ **Learning Objectives**

🖐 **Activities**

To identify the range of things (factors) affecting a situation.

5 minutes

Use Investigating Factors OHT 2 to introduce a question that could be practically investigated.

Discuss the meaning of the word 'affect'. It is best if a familiar context is used here. For example, *'Name the things that might affect what kind of day you have today?' 'Name the things that might affect what clothes you put on in the morning?'* These ideas can then be linked to how scientific investigations can be affected by many things. Ask the pupils to spend two minutes in groups deciding which things might affect the question.

To understand the word 'factor'.

5 minutes

Discuss the pupils' ideas using Investigating Factors OHT 3. This is more effective if Post-its are placed over the boxes and removed as ideas emerge. Introduce the term 'factor'.

Ask pupils to choose a factor to investigate. Name this as the 'Thing/factor being changed'.

To identify the factors affecting questions.

10 minutes

Using Investigating Factors OHT 4, ask pupils in groups to identify the factors that might affect the first question.

Pupils can record their answers to this question by either of the following:
● Writing on Post-its and sticking them on to their Planning Card.
● Writing out the answers on Pupil Sheet: Forming Questions (pages 9–11).

Discuss pupils' answers and ask them to choose which factor they would like to investigate. Ask pupils to attempt the remaining two questions.

To identify the factor that could be measured.

5 minutes

Use Investigating Factors OHT 5 to introduce the idea that scientists decide what they are going to look for, or measure, to find the answer to their question.

Stress the point that scientists try to identify the thing that will best answer their original question, not to list all of the things that they might have to measure in the course of their experiments – this is a common mistake.

Ask pupils to make their suggestions before Investigating Factors OHT 6 is used to demonstrate the answer.

To discuss the answers to the examples given.

5 minutes

Discuss the examples and remind pupils of the concepts they have learned.

Being a scientist

Scientists are often given questions to try to answer.

There are lots of ways they can try to do this.

I love having questions to answer!

Think about the following examples and decide how you would try to find out the answers.

How would you find out:

1. Which type of tree grows in your school grounds?

2. Which type of material will dry quickest when placed on a radiator?

3. How many Smarties can fit into a tube?

4. How heavy is your cat?

5. Is it true that the more sweets you eat, the more fillings your teeth will need?

Katie is a young scientist with a question to answer:

I want to find out what things might affect how quickly a piece of ice will melt.

Help Katie to work out which things might make the ice melt quicker or slower.

I want to find out what things might affect how quickly a piece of ice will melt.

Things (factors) I could change:

How hot the room is	How big the piece of ice is	The shape of the piece of ice

The thing (factor) I will change:

Use your Planning Card to decide how to investigate some of the questions below:

1. What might affect how far a football will travel when it is kicked?

2. What might affect how long a piece of cotton wool will take to fall to the ground?

3. What might affect how much air it will take to blow up a balloon until it bursts?

Now Katie has another problem:

What can I look at or measure to find out how quickly the ice melts?

The thing (factor) I am going to change:

How hot the room is

The thing (factor) I am going to measure:

How long it takes the ice to melt

Forming Questions

My question

What things might affect how far a football will travel when it is kicked?

The things (factors) I could change

_____

_____

_____

_____

_____

_____

The thing (factor) I will change

_____

The thing (factor) I will measure

_____

Investigating Factors Pupil Sheet

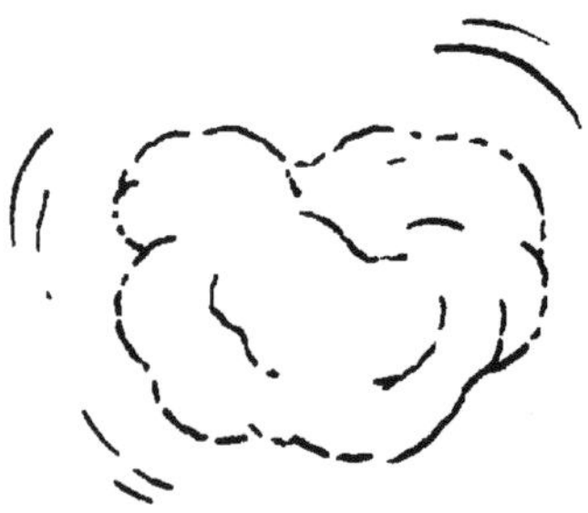

My question

What things might affect how long a piece of cotton wool will take to fall to the ground?

The things (factors) I could change

The thing (factor) I will change

The thing (factor) I will measure

My question

What things might affect how much air it will take to blow up a balloon until it bursts?

The things (factors) I could change

_____

_____

_____

_____

_____

_____

The thing (factor) I will change

_____

The thing (factor) I will measure

_____

What affects the growth of cress seedlings?
An application of Investigating Factors

Teacher page

▶ Aims

- To reinforce the skills of identifying possible factors for investigation.
- To recognise that plant growth is affected by the amount of water, temperature and light.

↻ Background Information

🗍 Resources

- Several small dishes of cress seedlings sown three to four days in advance and kept in moist, light conditions
- Measuring cylinders
- Access to a dark cupboard
- Planning Card (pages 41–42) or Planning Sheet (pages 43–44)
- Pupil Investigation Booklet (after page 44).

This session applies the skills learned in Investigating Factors to the scientific context of plant growth; **QCA Unit 3B**: Helping Plants Grow Well.

The growth of plants is affected by a number of factors as outlined below:

Water	Up to a point, the more water given to a plant the better it will grow. Water is used in photosynthesis to make food. Lack of water results in wilting and eventually death.
Light	Provides the energy to react water from the soil and carbon dioxide from the air to make food. Lack of light results in the plant turning yellow and growing tall and spindly as it searches for light (etiolation).
A suitable temperature	This aids the chemical reactions of photosynthesis. Cold temperatures result in slow growth; warm temperatures (up to about 40°C) encourage growth; hotter temperatures may kill a plant.

Where QCA units have been followed, pupils will already have investigated the effects of water on plant growth. Use your discretion regarding whether to give pupils a free choice of factor to investigate or to guide their decision.

➡ Learning Objectives

Activities

To identify the range of possible factors for investigation.	Show the class some dishes of cress seedlings. Tell pupils that they have been hired by Mr P Smith, the manager of a local cress company, to try to answer the question, *'What things affect how well cress seedlings grow?'*
10 minutes	Ask pupils to work in groups using a Planning Card or Planning Sheet to identify the factors that could be changed.
	Discuss the factors identified (if necessary prompt pupils regarding warmth). Decide as a class which factor to investigate.
To plan the investigation.	Suggest a plan for the investigation in which there is no control, for example, one tray of seedlings in the dark only. Ask pupils to say why this plan would not help answer the question.
5 minutes	Ask pupils to spend two minutes in groups trying to decide how to test the cress seedlings. If necessary, prompt pupils to recognise it is both cold and dark in the fridge (if warmth is chosen as the factor for investigation).
	Discuss pupils' ideas emphasising that all other factors should be kept the same to keep the test fair.

What affects the growth of cress seedlings?
An application of Investigating Factors

Teacher page

 Learning Objectives

 Activities

Learning Objectives	Activities
To identify the measurements that can be taken.	Ask the pupils to decide which factor they could observe or measure to find out how levels of water, light or warmth affect growth (whichever has been changed).
5 minutes	Pupils may suggest a variety of factors including the shoot or root length of the seedlings, their colour, weight, etc.
	Ask the pupils to record the factor to be measured on a Planning Sheet.
To set up a fair test.	Pupils set up their investigations and record their plans.
20 minutes	Leave the dishes for a number of days in test conditions. Ensure that all seedlings are kept moist where warmth and light are being investigated.
To collect results.	After a suitable number of days, ask the pupils to look at the outcomes of the test and to write a report on what they have discovered for the cress company.
20 minutes	

Further investigations where this skill could be reinforced

QCA Unit 3a: *Teeth and Eating*
What factors might affect how quickly a child's tooth will decay?

QCA Unit 3c: *Characteristics of Materials*
What factors might affect how much water a paper towel can absorb?

QCA Unit 3d: *Rocks and Soils*
What factors might affect how much water drains through a sample of soil?

QCA Unit 3e: *Magnets and Springs*
What factors might affect how far a toy car is propelled by a rubber band?

QCA Unit 3f: *Light and Shadows*
What factors might affect the size of a shadow?

What Will Happen?

▶ Aims

- To show how to devise simple predictions.
- To base predictions on pre-existing knowledge.

📖 Resources

- OHP
- OHTs 1–3
- Post-its
- Pupil Sheet 1: Making Predictions (pages 19–20)
- Pupil Sheet 2: Saying Why (pages 21–22)
- Pupil Investigation Booklet (after page 44).

↻ Background Information

This session teaches pupils to make predictions that are based on pre-existing knowledge.

National Curriculum coverage
Pupils should be taught to:
2c Think about what might happen ... when deciding what to do.

Pupils will be expected to understand the terms, *'The factor I changed'* and *'The factor I measured'* as introduced in Investigating Factors.

➡ Learning Objectives

✋ Activities

To introduce the idea of a prediction.

5 minutes

Introduce the lesson by asking a range of everyday questions such as, *'What do you think will happen if the school fire bell rings?'* or *'What would happen if you always crossed the road without looking both ways first?'* Explain to the pupils that their answers are all examples of something that we call predictions.

Now ask, *'Why do we make predictions in everyday life?'* Pupils should appreciate that making predictions helps us to prepare for what might happen and to decide, in advance, what we would do about it.

Tell pupils that when scientists are asked to find answers to questions, they try to make predictions about what they think will happen before testing out their ideas practically.

Use the context provided by What Will Happen? OHT 1 to recap on the terms introduced in Investigating Factors. Ask *'Which is the factor being changed and which is the factor being measured in this example?'*

Ask pupils to spend a few minutes thinking about the question and discussing possible answers before opening the question up for class suggestions. Use What Will Happen? OHT 2 to consolidate pupils' ideas.

To practise the formation of predictions.

10 minutes

Ask the pupils to attempt the prediction examples on Pupil Sheet 1: Making Predictions (pages 19 and 20).

At the end of this activity, ask a variety of pupils to offer their predictions. Stress that no prediction is right or wrong – it is the process that is of primary importance.

What Will Happen?

 Learning Objectives

 Activities

Learning Objectives	Activities
To show that good predictions are based on something that the person knows. *5 minutes*	Use What Will Happen? OHT 3 (with the thought bubbles covered up with Post-its). Ask the pupils to try to explain why they thought that the smaller ice cream melted faster than the larger one. Remove the Post-it to show one example. Emphasise that a prediction should be based on something that the person already knows otherwise it is simply a guess.
To practise explaining predictions. *10 minutes*	Ask the pupils to attempt the examples on Pupil Sheet 2: Saying Why (pages 21 and 22). This exercise requires pupils to practise making predictions but this time with some accompanying explanations. Each of the examples given has taken its context from the QCA units for Year 2 and so should be familiar to all Year 3 pupils.
To discuss the predictions made by pupils. *10 minutes*	Discuss each of the exercises with alternative explanations being requested. Ask pupils to decide whether each explanation has been based on something the person knew or whether it was just a guess. You can extend this by introducing the idea that explanations are better when they are based on scientific knowledge. Throughout this section the important issue is not whether the prediction or explanation is correct, but whether it has been based on something the pupil knew.

Sam has a question that is troubling her.

If I buy a large ice cream, will it melt faster than if I buy a small one?

What do you think the answer is?

You might have come up with some answers like these:

You should always try to say why you made your prediction:

I think the small ice cream will melt quickest because last summer I bought a big ice cream for myself and a small one for my little brother Tom. Tom's ice cream melted before mine did.

Making Predictions

1. What do you predict will happen when a piece of chocolate is left lying in the hot summer sun?

I think that a piece of chocolate left lying in the hot summer sun

will _____

_____

2. What do you predict will happen to a bowl of water placed in a freezer?

I think that the water will _____

_____

_____

3. What do you predict will happen when a raw egg is cracked into a hot frying pan?

I think that a raw egg cracked into a hot frying pan will

_____

_____

4. What do you predict will happen to the brightness of a torch bulb when its batteries start to run out?

I think that the brightness of a torch bulb will

_____

when its batteries start to run out.

5. If Andrew cleaned his teeth every day and his sister Heidi only cleaned her teeth every week, who would you predict would need to see the dentist first?

I think that _____

would need to see the dentist first.

6. One house plant is kept in the dark and one in the light for a week. Which one would you predict would look the greenest?

I think that the plant kept in the _____

would look the greenest.

Teaching Investigative Skills Year 3   © Folens (copiable page)

Saying Why

1. What do you predict will happen when a bulb is connected with some wires to a battery?

I think that the bulb will

_____

I think that this will happen because

_____

_____

_____

2. What do you predict will happen to a football when it is burst with a pin?

I think that the ball will

_____

I think that this will happen because

_____

_____

3. John takes no exercise. His friend Pete is always playing sports and cycling on his bike. Who do you predict would be the healthiest?

I think that the healthiest boy will be

_____

I think that this is true because

_____

_____

_____

4. What do you predict will happen to a plant if you do not water it?

I think that the plant will

_____

I think that this will happen because

_____

_____

_____

What affects the drainage of different soils?
An application of What Will Happen?

Teacher page

▶ Aims

- To reinforce the skill of making predictions.
- To recognise that the drainage of water through soils depends on the particle structure of the soil.

☐ Resources

- Sandy soil
- Clay soil
- Yoghurt pots/plastic cups with small pieces of filter paper cut to fit in the inside base of the container
- Measuring cylinders
- Planning Card (pages 41–42) or Planning Sheet (pages 43–44)
- Pupil Investigation Booklet (after page 44)
- Timers
- Pupil Sheet 3: Gardener's Question Time (page 26).

↻ Background Information

This session applies the skills learned in What Will Happen to the scientific context of the drainage of soil; **QCA Unit 3D**: Rocks and Soils

Soils are made when rocks break down by a process called weathering. It follows that the type of soil present in an area depends on the rock from which it has been formed. These rocks account for the geographical variation in soils' properties. Most soils are made up of three main constituents, sand, clay and humus (the remains of decomposed plants and animals, which gives soil its fertility). The variation in soil type is caused by changes in the proportions of these three substances.

Sandy soil has a light texture and excellent drainage due to the large particle size leaving gaps for water to flow through; it is permeable.

Clay soil, in contrast, has a heavy texture and poor drainage due to the small particles leaving small gaps. Most soils represent a mid-way point between these two extremes.

Loam is a good soil for growing things in as it contains moderate amounts of sand and clay with a large amount of humus.

Where QCA units have been followed, pupils will have already examined sandy soil, clay soil and loam, with particular emphasis on the size of particles.

→ Learning Objective

To revise the following facts:
Soils are formed when rocks are broken down by weathering processes.
All soils contain sand, clay and humus in different proportions.

10 minutes

Activities

Ask the pupils to spend some time in groups trying to answer the following questions:
- Where does soil come from?
- What is the difference between sandy and clay soil?

Discuss the answers with the class. Draw diagrams of sandy soil and clay soil showing the variation in particle size.

What affects the drainage of different soils?
An application of What Will Happen?

 Learning Objectives

 Activities

Learning Objectives	Activities
To identify the factors that might affect the drainage of water through soil. *10 minutes*	Revise the meaning of the term, 'permeable'. Explain that the pupils are going to carry out an investigation into what affects the amount of water that can drain through soil. Ask the pupils to use a Planning Card (pages 41–42) or Planning Sheet (pages 43–44) to identify the factors that may have an effect. Possible suggestions: ● Type of soil ● Amount of soil ● Amount of water ● How hot or cold the soil is ● The type of container the soil is held in. Discuss possible factors and decide on one factor to change – type of soil. Discuss pupils' ideas on how the amount of water draining through a sample of soil could be measured (for example, the total amount of water draining through the sample of soil in 1 minute).
To make a scientific prediction. *10 minutes*	Give each pupil a copy of the Pupil Investigation Booklet (after page 44). Ask the pupils to use their Pupil Investigation Booklet to predict whether sandy or clay soil would allow most water to drain through and to back this up with an explanation. You may wish to tell pupils that they should use ideas of particle size (as covered earlier in the QCA unit) or their everyday experience in the explanation. For example, *'I think that sandy soil will drain quicker than clay soil as I've seen water on a beach just disappear but the water in the fields next to my house is always forming puddles'.* Discuss pupils' predictions but give no indication regarding whether they are correct.
To plan and carry out a test. *20 minutes*	Plan the investigation as a class before asking pupils to carry it out. Alternatively you may wish to carry out the investigation as a class demonstration with pupils taking part. A suitable technique is outlined below: ● Make some small drainage holes in the base of two yoghurt pots or plastic beakers. ● Place a circular piece of filter paper in the base of each container. ● Fill the containers with 4cm depth of each type of soil and place each container over an empty container (to collect drained water). ● Pour in 25ml of water measured in a measuring cylinder. ● Collect the drained water and measure it using a measuring cylinder.
To show that different soils have different levels of permeability due to variations in particle size. *5 minutes*	Look at the results of the investigation and discuss whether pupils' predictions were correct.

What affects the drainage of different soils?
An application of What Will Happen?

→ Learning Objective

To apply the information gained in the lesson to common gardening problems.

5 minutes

 Activity

Ask pupils to apply their new-found knowledge by completing Pupil Sheet 3: Gardener's Question Time (page 26) on some common gardening problems.

Further investigations where this skill could be reinforced

QCA Unit 3a: *Teeth and Eating*
Predict the roles carried out by the different types of teeth.

QCA Unit 3b: *Helping Plants Grow Well*
Predict how the growth of plants is affected by different environmental conditions, e.g. light, water, temperature.

QCA Unit 3c: *Characteristics of Materials*
Predict which type of paper towel is most absorbent.
Predict which tights are most stretchy.

QCA Unit 3e: *Magnets and Springs*
Predict what will happen to the movement of a toy car propelled by a rubber band as the band is stretched further.
Predict whether some mystery objects will be attracted to a magnet or not.

QCA Unit 3f: *Light and Shadows*
Predict what will happen to the direction and length of a shadow over the course of a day.
Predict what will happen when a torch is shone on a material – investigation in transparent, translucent and opaque materials.

Gardener's Question Time

Mr Potter has a garden in which he grows all sorts of vegetables. However, the different vegetables he wants to grow all need slightly different types of soil:

- Lettuce needs soil that drains well.

- Marrow needs soil that holds plenty of water.

- Carrots need soil with lots of nutrients.

- Broad beans will grow in any soil.

Mr Potter has bought some sand, clay soil and peat (soil rich in humus), but he does not know what to do with it!

Suggest how Mr Potter could improve his soil for:

1. Growing lettuce _____

_____

2. Growing marrows _____

_____

3. Growing carrots _____

_____

4. Growing broad beans _____

_____

Teaching Investigative Skills Year 3

Fair Tests

▶ Aims

- To recognise whether or not a test is fair.
- To identify those factors to be controlled in a fair test.

☐ Resources

- OHP
- OHTs 1–7
- Pupil Sheet: Fair Testing (pages 37–38)
- Pupil Investigation Booklet (after page 44)
- Rope
- Backpack
- Stopwatch.

↻ Background Information

This session teaches pupils how to plan a fair test (changing only one factor while controlling the rest) to investigate their predictions.

National Curriculum coverage
Pupils should be taught to:
2d Make a fair test or comparison by changing one factor and observing or measuring the effect while keeping other factors the same.

Fair tests are introduced using the familiar context of sporting competitions. However, it is vital that teachers recognise that it is impossible to carry out a fair test, in its strictest sense, where living organisms are concerned, as no two individuals are identical.

However, at this level, sport is only being used as a familiar context to introduce the idea that scientific tests should not be unfair if they are to produce trustworthy outcomes.

Pupils commonly make one of two mistakes with fair testing:
- Changing more than one factor at a time.
- Trying to keep everything the same rather than just the key factors.

→ Learning Objective

To introduce the idea of a fair test using examples from sport.

15 minutes

🖐 Activities

For a fun and active start to the lesson place a loaded backpack on one pupil, tie a rope around another pupil's legs and leave a third unhindered (make sure all three pupils can move comfortably and safely). Say to the class, *'We want to find out which of these three pupils is the fastest runner. Who do you think would win the race?'* Ask the three pupils to try to cover an agreed distance one by one, timing them using a stopwatch.

Alternatively, use Fair Tests OHT 1 to introduce the idea of a fair test in a more controlled context. An example from sports is provided where pupils are asked to predict who would win a 100m race.

Both of these contexts provide the opportunity for pupils to revise the skills of prediction taught in What Will Happen?

Ask the pupils the question, *'Can you really be sure that the fastest runner won the race? Was the test fair?'* Challenge pupils to make a list of the ways in which the test was unfair.

Fair Tests

→ **Learning Objective**

Activities

Possible answers may include:
- They should be wearing the same clothes.
- They should all have the same shoes on.
- They should all be free to run without anything holding them back.

Use the two examples on Fair Tests OHTs 2 and 3 to provoke further class discussion. A deliberate attempt has been made to keep the early contexts science-free to allow pupils to consolidate this concept before applying it to investigative situations.

In the examples provided, the competitions would be unfair because:
- Nick has a snorkel and flippers to help him to swim underwater whereas Barry does not.
- Nick is wearing goggles that may give him the advantage of seeing where he is going.
- Torfinn has a lower basket to get his ball in compared to Joel.
- Joel has a larger basket to get his ball in compared to Torfinn.

To apply the ideas of fair testing to the scientific context.

10 minutes

Make the point that, in the same way as we could not tell which runner really was the fastest, we cannot be sure of the answer to a scientific question unless the test is fair.

Ask the pupils to look at the context presented on Fair Tests OHT 4 and to identify the factor being changed (the temperature of the room) and the factor being measured (how quickly the ice melts).

Set the pupils the problem of listing the factors to be controlled to make the test fair. Allow a short amount of time for pupils to discuss their answers before feeding their ideas back to the class. Use Fair Tests OHT 5 to consider the answers.

Use Fair Tests OHTs 6 and 7 to practise identifying unfair tests. Give the pupils a few minutes to work out each example. Ask the pupils to discuss the situations first within their groups, before considering their answers in a whole class discussion.

Answers:
- Fair Tests OHT 6: Different types of ball, different landing surfaces.
- Fair Tests OHT 7: Different sizes or quantities of material, different amounts of water to soak up.

Fair Tests

→ Learning Objectives

 Activities

To practise the skills of planning a fair test.

10 minutes

Ask the pupils to complete the examples on Pupil Sheet: Fair Testing (pages 37–38). Each of the examples has taken its context from the QCA units for Years 2 and 3 and so should be familiar to all Year 3 pupils. These exercises require pupils to identify the factors to be controlled in some simple contexts. Encourage pupils to work together on these exercises and to discuss their answers in groups.

Answers:
1. Amount of water; temperature; surface grown on.
2. Amount of milk; left at the same temperature; in the same type of container.
3. Temperature of tea to begin with; amount of tea; temperature of room.
4. Number of batteries; length of wire; age of batteries; thickness of wire.

To discuss the predictions made by pupils.

5 minutes

Discuss each of the exercises in turn. Ask the pupils to add any factors they missed to their lists.

Look at the pictures of the three people.
In a 100m race, who do you think will be able to
run the fastest?

Bert the
businessman

Fred the
firefighter

Tim the
teacher

Do all of the runners
have the same chance
to win the race?

A competition to see who can swim the longest underwater.

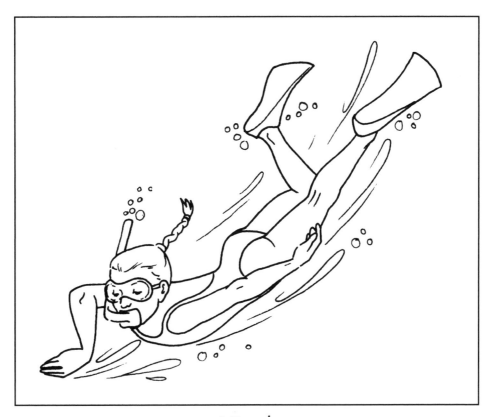

Nicola

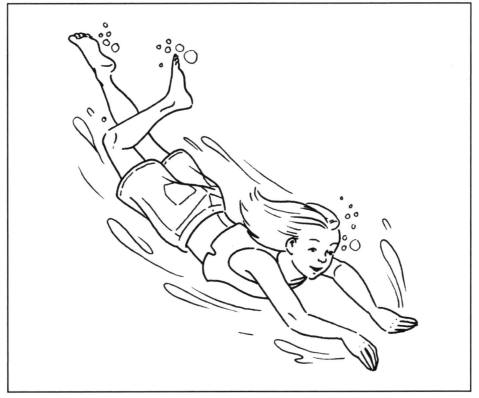

Belinda

A competition to see who can score the most baskets.

Torfinn

Joel

David wants to find out if the temperature of a room will affect how quickly or slowly a piece of ice will melt.

What should I keep the same?

He decides to do the following things:

- Put a piece of ice in a cold room.
- Put another piece of ice in a warm room.
- Time each piece of ice with a stopwatch to see how long they take to melt.

Make a list of the things David will have to keep the same to make sure that the test is fair.

Jackie wants to find out whether the height that a ball is dropped from affects how high it will bounce.

She drops balls from different heights and measures how high they bounce.

How fair is the test?

Annabel wants to find out which of two pieces of kitchen towel will absorb the most water.

- First, Annabel weighs each piece of material.

- Then she puts them in some water.

- Finally she weighs them again to see which has gained most mass.

How fair is this test?

Fair Testing

1. You want to find out whether a sunflower seed or a cress seed will germinate the fastest. You plant each seed. What things will you need to keep the same to make your test fair?

    I would keep the following things the same:

    _____

    _____

    _____

    _____

2. You want to find out which of two types of milk will keep fresh for the longest. What things will you need to keep the same to make your test fair?

    I would keep the following things the same:

    _____

    _____

    _____

    _____

3. You have a plastic teacup and a china teacup. You want to find out which cup will keep tea hot for longest. What things will you need to keep the same to make your test fair?

I would keep the following things the same:

_____

_____

_____

_____

_____

4. You have three identical electric light bulbs and some 1.5V batteries. You want to find out whether the number of bulbs will affect their brightness when connected in a circuit. What things will you need to keep the same to make your test fair?

I would keep the following things the same:

_____

_____

_____

_____

What affects how much water a kitchen towel can soak up? An application of Fair Tests

▶ Aim

● To reinforce the skill of planning fair tests.

☐ Resources

● Three types of kitchen towel
● Measuring cylinders
● Dishes to hold water
● Pupil Investigation Booklet (after page 44)
● Planning Card (pages 41–42) or Planning Sheet (pages 43–44).

↻ Background Information

This session applies the skills of planning a fair test to the context of investigating the absorbency levels of kitchen towels; **QCA Unit 3C**: Characteristics of Materials. Since the key idea of this investigation is reinforcement, direct the class to investigate the same key factor – type of kitchen towel.

→ Learning Objectives

✌ Activities

Learning Objectives	Activities
To identify the factors that might affect how much water a kitchen towel can soak up. *10 minutes*	Explain to the pupils that the head teacher has asked them to investigate which type of kitchen towel would be the best one for the school to buy to mop up the coffee that gets spilled in the staff room. Ask the pupils to use a Planning Card or Planning Sheet to identify the factors that might affect how much water a kitchen towel can soak up. Possible answers may include the following: • Size of kitchen towel • Make of towel • Amount of water • Temperature of water • Thickness of towel. Discuss the range of possible factors with the class. Select 'Type of kitchen towel' as the factor to be changed. Allow pupils to look at and feel the range of kitchen towels available for investigation.
To make a scientific prediction. *5 minutes*	Ask the pupils to use their Pupil Investigation Booklets (after page 44) to predict which kitchen towel would absorb the most water and to explain how they came to their decision. Discuss the pupils' predictions, being careful not to give any indication of whether they might be correct or not.
To plan a fair test. *10 minutes*	Ask the pupils to spend 2 minutes deciding how to test a variety of kitchen towels to find out which can soak up the most water. Discuss their plans and list an agreed sequence of actions to be followed by all groups. For example: 1. Measure 25ml of water into a bowl using a measuring cylinder. 2. Place a piece of kitchen towel in the water until it is soaked through. 3. Take the kitchen towel out of the water and hold it until the water has stopped dripping off.

What affects how much water a kitchen towel can soak up? An application of Fair Tests

→ Learning Objectives

4. Pour the remaining water back into the measuring cylinder.
5. Write down how much water is left in the bowl.

Carry out the sequence of actions with the pupils taking part.

Ask the pupils to list the things that they will have to keep the same each time the test is carried out to make sure that the test is fair. Suggestions should include the following:

● Size of kitchen towel – cut to agreed size (10cm x 10cm).
● Amount of water – measured with a measuring cylinder.
● Amount of time kitchen towel is left to drip for – timed with a stopwatch or timer.

To carry out a fair test. *20 minutes*	Ask the pupils to work in groups to carry out the fair test and record their results.
To consider results and draw conclusions. *15 minutes*	Collect the class data and display the results in a table on the board. Ask the pupils to suggest why some groups might have found a different kitchen towel soaked up the most water (i.e. the test was not carried out totally fairly). Ask the pupils to write a report explaining the fair test and giving a recommendation for the head teacher. Alternatively, ask the head teacher to visit the classroom to hear the findings from a group or groups of pupils.

Further investigations where this skill could be reinforced

QCA Unit 3a: *Teeth and Eating*
Do electric toothbrushes clean teeth better than normal toothbrushes?
(Use disclosing tablets).

QCA Unit 3b: *Helping Plants Grow Well*
What affect does warmth have on plant growth?

QCA Unit 3d: *Rocks and Soils*
Which is the hardest rock? What affects the drainage of water through soil?

QCA Unit 3e: *Magnets and Springs*
Which is the strongest magnet? Which materials will magnets work through?

QCA Unit 3f: *Light and Shadows*
What affects the size of a shadow?

Planning Card

I want to find out:

_____

_____

Things (factors) I could change:

The thing (factor) I will change:

Planning Card

The thing (factor) I will change:

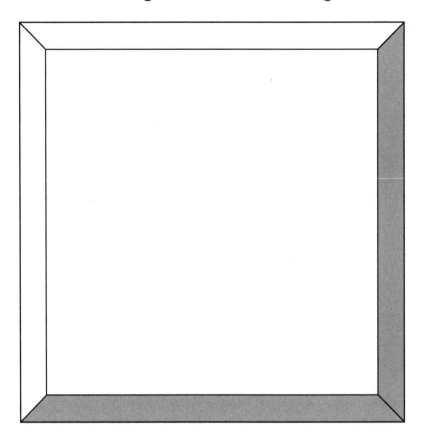

The thing (factor) I will measure:

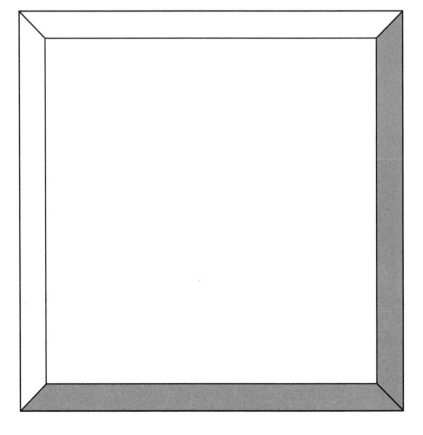

Teaching Investigative Skills Year 3 © Folens (copiable page)

Planning Sheet

My question:

I want to find out: _____

_____

Things (factors) I could change:

_____

_____

_____

_____

_____

_____

_____

The thing (factor) I will change:

_____

The thing (factor) I will measure:

_____

HOW TO CREATE ...
Your Guide to Science Investigations Booklet

STEP 1

Photocopy the title page.

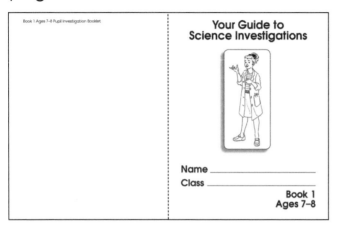

STEP 2

On the back of the title page photocopy pages 2 and 7.

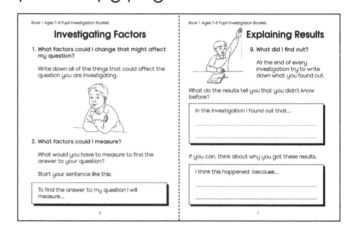

STEP 3

Photocopy pages 6 and 3.

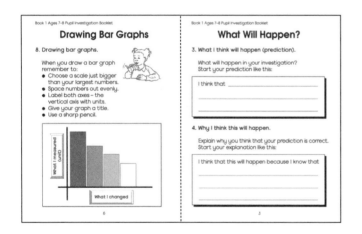

STEP 4

On the back of pages 6 and 3 photocopy pages 4 and 5.

STEP 5

Put the copied sheets together to make the booklet.

Staple if necessary.

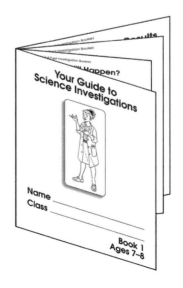

Your Guide to Science Investigations

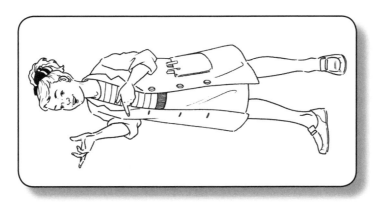

Name

Class

**Book 1
Ages 7–8**

Investigating Factors

1. What factors could I change that might affect my question?

Write down all of the things that could affect the question you are investigating.

2. What factors could I measure?

What would you have to measure to find the answer to your question?

Start your sentence like this:

To find the answer to my question I will measure...

Explaining Results

9. What did I find out?

At the end of every investigation try to write down what you found out.

What do the results tell you that you didn't know before?

In this investigation I found out that...

If you can, think about why you got these results.

I think this happened because...